VAMPIRE KNIGHT

Story & Art by
Matsuri
Hino

Vol. 2

The Story of
VAMPIRE KNIGHT

1 Cross Academy, the distinguished private boarding school, has a Day Class for ordinary students and a Night Class for vampires.

The elite Night Class students are all vampires!

The existence of vampires and the truth behind the Night Class is kept secret from Day Class students, who unknowingly coexist with them.

THERE IS A SECRET THAT THE DAY CLASS DOES NOT KNOW.

THE NIGHT CLASS CONSISTS ENTIRELY OF VAMPIRES.

I'LL GET YOU FOR THIS.

WHAT DID I DO?

WE ARE THE GUARDIANS OF THE SCHOOL.

2 Yuki is the adopted daughter of the Headmaster of Cross Academy. She has no memories of herself prior to age 5. Zero loathes vampires after his family was killed by one. The two childhood friends are School Guardians who protect the secret of the Night Class!

FANGS PROTRUDING OBSCENELY FROM HIS LIPS...

3 Zero had actually been bitten by a pureblood vampire!

For four years, Zero had been resisting his vampire instincts, suffering greatly. But he eventually sinks his fangs into Yuki! Zero blames himself and tries to leave the school, but Yuki stops him, deciding to be his ally...

✤ Purebloods vampires are vampires who do not have a single drop of human blood in their lineage. They are very powerful, and they can turn humans into vampires by drinking their blood.

NIGHT CLASS

DAY CLASS

CLASSMATE

KANAME KURAN
Night Class President and pureblood vampire. Yuki adores him.

YUKI CROSS
The heroine.
The adopted daughter of the Headmaster, and a Guardian who protects Cross Academy.

YORI
Yuki's best friend.

ZERO KIRYU
Yuki's childhood friend, and a Guardian.
His family was killed by a vampire a very long time ago.

NIGHT CLASS STUDENTS

FOSTER FATHER

COUSINS

HEADMASTER CROSS
He raised Yuki.
He is trying to educate the students to become a bridge between humans and vampires.

HANABUSA AIDO
Nickname: Idol

AKATSUKI KAIN
Nickname: Wild

...SHOOT ME WITH THAT GUN.

What is to be their fate?!

...AND GO MAD AS A VAMPIRE...

IF I LOSE THE HUMAN PART OF ME...

VAMPIRE KNIGHT

Contents

VAMPIRE KNIGHT

...

YOU MUST'VE BEEN REALLY WORRIED ABOUT HER.

NO WAY!

THAT WAS COLD!

WELL, I'M OFF TO READ MORE MANGA...

TMP TMP

ICHIJO.

SUFF

SIGH

WHAT WOULD YOU LIKE ME TO DO...

...KANA-ME?

LU NK...

OH. ...

HE'S COOKING FOR US.

HM. THE HEADMASTER ASKED US TO GET... LET'S SEE...

BEEF LIVER, BOK CHOY...

TUG

ZERO! HEY, LOOK!

UHH...

THERE'S MORE?

YOU DON'T HAVE TO WORRY. THE NIGHT CLASS HAS TODAY OFF SO THEY WON'T BE COMING OUT OF THEIR DORM.

WE SHOULD GET BACK TO THE SCHOOL BEFORE SUNSET.

HEY...

GIMME YOUR ARM.

IF I LEAVE YOU ALONE, ZERO, YOU DON'T TAKE CARE OF YOURSELF AT ALL...

YOU NEED SOMEONE TO CHOOSE FOR YOU.

HM.

GOOD.

YOU'RE LIKE...

HEE HEE

...A YOUNGER BROTHER WHO NEEDS LOOKING AFTER.

YOU GET ANGRY SO EASILY!

OH?

YOU'RE MAD.

SWIP

YOU'RE A YEAR YOUNGER THAN I AM.

I'M SO APPALLED THAT I FIND IT FUNNY.

YOU'RE A YEAR OLDER THAN I AM, BUT YOU CUT SCHOOL-- THAT'S WHY WE'RE IN THE SAME CLASS!

WHEN WE FIRST MET, YOU WERE ABOUT THE SAME HEIGHT AS I WAS!

PLEASE GIVE ME THE CHANGE QUICKLY!

GR'RRR

HA!

...AND YOU'RE ACTING LIKE A "BIG SIS"?

YOU LOOK LIKE A GRADE-SCHOOLER...

THAT'S HILARIOUS.

HURRY UP OR I'LL LEAVE YOU BEHIND...

AH!

..."BIG SIS."

IT'S ONLY FOR ZERO ANYWAY.

YOU DON'T HAVE TO WRAP IT.

I'LL TAKE THIS ONE.

...MAKES ME FEEL LIKE WE'VE RETURNED TO THE OLD DAYS SOMEWHAT.

BEING LIKE THIS...

YEAH.

ZERO IS ZERO.

...A VAMPIRE NOW...

EVEN IF YOU ARE...

I'LL TREAT YOU FOR CARRYING ALL THAT STUFF.

ZERO, YOU EAT SOMETHING TOO.

...

I CAN'T LOOK HIM IN THE EYE NOW...

WELL, I LOVE THE PARFAIT HERE, SO...

YORI AND I CAME HERE LAST TIME...

I WANTED TO EAT SHIO RAMEN.

OH!

SHE TOOK HIM TO A CAFÉ WITHOUT ASKING.

HOFF

I KNOW YOU'RE AFRAID TO.

...

I CAN!

YOU STILL...

...CAN'T GO OUTSIDE SCHOOL GROUNDS ALONE...

SHUT UP!

KLANK

I'M NOT AFRAID OF WHAT HAPPENED TEN YEARS AGO.

...THAT NOT ALL VAMPIRES ARE "WELL-BEHAVED" LIKE KANAME KURAN...

IF YOU GO OUTSIDE THE SCHOOL...

...YOU REMEMBER, DON'T YOU...

SHMP SLSH MP

YOU EAT A LOT.

SHUT UP!

WHY ARE YOU OUTSIDE...

...DOING THIS?

GO BACK QUICKLY AND GET YOUR WOUND TREATED.

NOT NOW, YUKI.

YOUR BLOOD IS TOO PROVOCATIVE FOR US.

GRIP

B-BMP

I REALIZE...

...THERE'S STILL SO MUCH I DON'T KNOW.

SIXTH NIGHT/END

VAMPIRE KNIGHT

SEVENTH NIGHT: NIGHT PARTY

VAMPIRES, THOSE BEASTS IN HUMAN FORM WHO DRINK THE BLOOD FROM LIVING HUMANS...

...VAMPIRE HUNTERS...

...THOSE WHO ARE FATED TO HUNT VAMPIRES...

...AND...

THERE ARE THOSE WHO EXIST IN THE DARKNESS...

BONITO, LIGHTLY GRILLED, WITH CHOPPED CELERY AND PERILLA SAUCE, MY STYLE.

AND MUCH MORE.

A MELT-IN-YOUR-MOUTH STEW OF BOK CHOY AND FILET, MY STYLE.

STIR-FRIED LIVER AND LEEKS, MY STYLE.

HOW IS IT? GOOD?

...

SILENCE

WELL, IT'S ALL RIGHT... YOU'RE EATING IT...

MNCH

MNCH

...

GLOOM MOMMY IS SAD!!

WAAAH!

I TRIED SO HARD TO COOK GOOD FOOD!

IT'S BEEN A WHILE SINCE THE FAMILY HAS HAD DINNER TOGETHER.

I KEEP TELLING YOU NOT TO CONSIDER ME AS PART OF YOUR FAMILY.

I KEEP TELLING YOU THAT YOUR "MY STYLE" COOKING IS A BIT OFF.

HE TOLD US TO GUARD YOU SO THAT OUR GUYS DON'T MESS WITH YOU.

UNFORTUNATELY, TONIGHT...

YEAH...

...ONLY BECAUSE ICHIJO ASKED US TO.

...ALMOST ALL OF THE NIGHT CLASS STUDENTS...

...ARE HERE ON THE MOON DORM GROUNDS.

ZAA

I WOULDN'T IF I WERE YOU.

YOU'LL GO DOWN FIRST.

TING

...

HMPH, THEY CAME?

WHAT FOR?

PLEASE ENJOY YOURSELVES!

TONIGHT IS MY BIRTHDAY PARTY!

THIS CORNER IS A WORLD OF ITS OWN.

H-HOW OLD ARE YOU?

SHE ASKS BECAUSE SHE THINKS IT'S EXPECTED OF HER.

HE'S TOO MUCH LIKE A HUMAN AND NOT ENOUGH LIKE A VAMPIRE...

JUST HIM, THOUGH.

HUH?!

...I WANT YOU TO KISS ME FOR MY BIRTHDAY PRESENT, YUKI!

I'M EIGHTEEN. I'M A GROWNUP NOW! OH...

...VAMPIRE YEARS?

V...

HOW OLD IN HUMAN YEARS OR VAMPIRE YEARS?

...THAT VAMPIRE...

I CAN'T LOOK THE OTHER WAY. LEAVING SCHOOL GROUNDS WITHOUT PERMISSION IS AGAINST SCHOOL RULES...

...AND... MORE- OVER...

OH, THAT.

SHE'S NOT OKAY HERE AT ALL.

UM!

AS MEMBERS OF THE DISCIPLINARY COMMITTEE, WE WANT TO KNOW WHAT HAPPENED TODAY.

WE CAME HERE ON BUSINESS.

ASK ME ANYTHING.

SURE.

EVERYONE HERE KNOWS ABOUT IT.

THERE'S NO WAY WE COULD ALLOW A DANGEROUS VAMPIRE LIKE THAT TO ROAM FREELY IN THE TOWN...

...BUT YOU TWO WENT TO THE TROUBLE OF KILLING IT.

WHY THAT VAMPIRE?

AIDO!

...

THAT VAMPIRE USED TO BE HUMAN.

YUKI, VAMPIRES...

...ARE RULED BY A FEW PUREBLOODS AND A HANDFUL OF ARISTOCRATS.

EVERY STUDENT IN THE NIGHT CLASS IS AN ARISTOCRAT OR HIGHER...

FILTHY THINGS.

<LEVEL C>
COMMON VAMPIRES

<LEVEL D>
FORMER HUMANS

<LEVEL E>

THE VAMPIRE I KILLED...

...WAS A LEVEL E VAMPIRE-- A VAMPIRE WHO'S FALLEN OUTSIDE THE PYRAMID.

LEVEL E?

...FORMER HUMANS ARE LOWER THAN COMMON VAMPIRES.

TO USE A PYRAMID AS AN EXAMPLE...

<LEVEL A>
PUREBLOODS

<LEVEL B>
ARISTOCRATS

TO TELL THE TRUTH, THEY AREN'T TREATED VERY WELL.

<LEVEL C>
COMMON VAMPIRES

<LEVEL D>
FORMER HUMANS

ZERO IS?

"LEVEL: END" TO BE EXACT.

...SO HE SHOULD KNOW ALL THIS.

KIRYU IS A MEMBER OF A VAMPIRE HUNTER FAMILY...

BUT...

...EVENTUALLY FALL INTO THE LEVEL E CATEGORY, YUKI.

FORMER HUMANS...

THEY GRADUALLY LOSE THEIR SANITY, REACHING THE "END"-- THEIR DESTRUCTION.

YES... IN THEIR ENDLESS THIRST FOR BLOOD...

...THEY START ATTACKING PEOPLE INDISCRIMINATELY.

THAT IS WHY FORMER HUMANS ARE MANAGED BY THE ARISTOCRATS AND ABOVE.

M-MANAGED...?

BUT ACCIDENTS DO OCCUR.

A MAD VAMPIRE MAY FLEE FROM AN ARISTO-CRAT...

...AND WANDER INTO HUMAN SOCIETY.

THERE WAS A REPORT THAT A LEVEL E VAMPIRE WOULD APPEAR IN TOWN TODAY.

ICHIJO AND SHIKI HUNTED IT DOWN...

ZAA

...THAT VAMPIRE TO BE...

YOU ORDERED...

YUKI.

WHY DIDN'T YOU INFORM THE HEAD-MASTER?

FIRSTHAND, HUH...

I DIDN'T THINK IT WAS SOMETHING I SHOULD REPORT...

YOU'RE A MEMBER OF THE DISCIPLINARY COMMITTEE, YET WHEN ICHIJO IN-VITED YOU, YOU CAME HERE...

BUT!

...AND I WANTED TO KNOW THE TRUTH FIRST-HAND.

YUKI, KIRYU...

...COME OVER HERE.

...TO A DANGEROUS PLACE LIKE THIS.

ZERO...

I SAID SOMETHING I SHOULDN'T HAVE.

...VUP

CROSSING

CHK

THAT WAS SCARY.

YEAH...I WILL *TRY* NOT TO WHILE I'M AT THIS SCHOOL...

...I DON'T WANT TO HINDER THE HEADMASTER'S PACIFIST IDEOLOGY.

NOW, NOW, AIDO...

...DON'T REALLY DO IT.

TEARING HIM INTO SHREDS RIGHT HERE WOULDN'T BE ENOUGH.

KIRYU POINTED THAT GUN AT KANAME-SAMA...

GRIP

I HAVEN'T SEEN HIM...

...FOR FOUR YEARS.

I DIDN'T THINK I'D BE ABLE TO SEE HIM AGAIN.

IT MAY HAVE BEEN A MISTAKE TO LEAVE HIM IN YOUR CARE.

WHAT ARE YOU SAYING?

YOU HAD NO OTHER CHOICE.

DID YOU DO YOUR "WORK"?

OH REALLY?

...A LEVEL E WANDERED INTO TOWN.

TODAY...

THEY WON'T FOLLOW SUCH RULES!

HA HA HA!

THEY'RE THE ONLY ARISTOCRATS WHO CAN DO ANYTHING AROUND HERE.

DON'T PRETEND YOU DON'T KNOW.

WELL! I WONDER WHO IT WAS? SAVING OUR TOWN LIKE THAT!

WELL, THERE IS A SCHOOL RULE FORBIDDING THE NIGHT CLASS TO LEAVE SCHOOL GROUNDS WITHOUT PERMISSION.

THE NIGHT CLASS MUST HAVE SNATCHED IT.

THEY TURNED IT TO ASHES FIRST.

...

...

THIS ATMOS-PHERE IS...

KANAME.

I'M LEAVING NOW.

HEE HEE

HA HA HA

SIGH

GRIN GRIN

YOU WANT TO CUT IT, SHIKI?

WHAT A HUGE CAKE... YOU'RE EATING IT BY YOURSELF?

OF COURSE

HOLD THE CAKE FOR ME, ICHIJO.

THIS IS FOR EVERYONE.

UFFFF

VR

SHK SHK

HERE.

SHOULD YOU HAVE LET HER GO LIKE THAT?

IT'S ALL RIGHT...

...FOR NOW...

UHHHHH

THIS IS BORING TO DRINK.

TOO BAD.

SHIKI? DRINK *THIS* INSTEAD.

I HAVE NO INTENTION OF SERVING MYSELF TO YOU

GRIP

VAMPIRE KNIGHT

EIGHTH NIGHT: THE FORBIDDEN ACT

WHY DO VAMPIRES HURT HUMANS?

BECAUSE THEY ARE PITIFUL BEINGS WHO LIVE ONLY BY INSTINCT.

ZERO...

...YOU DO UNDERSTAND NOW?

VAMPIRE HUNTERS LIKE ME AND THE KIRYU FAMILY EXIST FOR THAT PURPOSE.

THAT'S WHY WE HUNT THEM.

VAMPIRES CAN ONLY EVER BE OUR ENEMY.

IV

↓ (continued) But there are lots of things that degrade Kaname-sama. ☠ I would never be able to reveal them, Because it would ruin his image. (←What did you try to make him do, Hino...?)

◆

The other day, my editor complimented me, saying that Zero's hand gestures look great and that Kaname's hand gestures look sexy ♡ I'm happy! ♡ But there is something I couldn't say then: To my editor and to all my readers... I apologize for ruining your fantasies... The model for those hands is...

TREMBLE

...me! My desperate hands.. The hands whose gestures were called lewd when I was small... (I changed my hands into male versions..) I'm sorry, Zero, Kaname-tama. (Did I ruin their image?)

I'M TOGA YAGARI.

I'M THE FORMER MASTER OF ZERO...

I'M A VAMPIRE HUNTER.

RIGHT, ZERO?

YOU REALLY ARE THE ADOPTED DAUGHTER OF THAT SILLY TWIT...

YES.

LET ME TAKE CARE OF THINGS...

...YOU GO HOME, YUKI.

...YET YOU CONSIDER ME AS YOUR ENEMY.

ZERO WAS ABOUT TO ATTACK YOU...

THEY WENT TO THE HEAD-MASTER'S ROOM...

I WAS THE ONE WHO WAS SHUT OUT.

THE HEADMASTER SAID THERE'S NOTHING TO WORRY ABOUT...

...BUT THAT MAN SAID HE'D KILL ZERO...

IF THINGS CONTINUE LIKE THIS, ZERO WILL...

ZERO CAN'T TOLERATE BLOOD TABLETS...

...SO HIS BODY WILL CONTINUE TO LUST FOR BLOOD...

YUKI?

OH!

I WOKE YOU UP. I'M SORRY...

AND HIS MIND IS BEING EATEN AWAY...

HIS WORDS ECHO IN MY HEAD.

IT'S ALL RIGHT.

ZERO DIDN'T COME TO SCHOOL.

HE'S NOT AT SCHOOL OR THE DORM. THE HEADMASTER ISN'T AROUND EITHER...

WHAT DID YOU DO TO HIM?!

WHAT HAPPENED TO ZERO?

GRAB

WE QUARANTINED HIM, OF COURSE.

WE QUARANTINED HIM SO THAT THERE WON'T BE ANY VICTIMS UNTIL I SETTLE THINGS.

HE'S TO THE POINT WHERE HE'LL ATTACK AT ANY TIME.

QUARANTINED...?

WHERE IS HE?!

BUT ZERO IS SAFE FOR NOW, RIGHT?

THAT RETIRED TWIT TOLD ME I WOULDN'T BE ABLE TO STAY HERE UNLESS I DID SOMETHING!

HE FORCED ME TO BECOME...

LET ME GO! I'VE GOT WORK TO DO!

TAK

TAK

TAK

BAM

I'M TOGA YAGARI. I'LL BE YOUR TEMPORARY LECTURER FOR THIS ETHICS CLASS.

NICE TO MEET YOU, VAMPIRES...

SO IT WAS YOU SHOOTING LAST NIGHT...

HE HAS THE SAME NAME AS THE MAN WHO'S THE NO. 1 VAMPIRE HUNTER RIGHT NOW...

"YAGARI"?

YOU'VE COME BACK TO CHECK OUT THE NIGHT CLASS?

I HEARD THAT YOU WERE SOMEWHERE FAR AWAY, BUT YOU'VE RETURNED?

RELAX.

TODAY I AM AN OFFICIAL TEACHER...

...WITH A TEACHING CERTIFI- CATE.

OR IS THERE A VAMPIRE AMONG US WHO YOU WANT TO KILL...

...TEACHER?

SHIFF

HEH...

I'LL BE CAREFUL...

HELLO, KANAME KURAN.

...TEACHER.

POK

IF YOU FALL ASLEEP BECAUSE MY LECTURE IS BORING, I CAN ADD YOU TO THE LIST, YOU KNOW?

UNFORTUNATELY MY EXECUTION LIST IS EMPTY RIGHT NOW.

KR EEK

YOU SAID ZERO WAS OKAY...

I THOUGHT YOU'D GO OFF TO FIND ZERO.

YOU WAITED ALL THIS TIME?

I WAS AFRAID THE NIGHT CLASS WOULD TEAR YOU TO SHREDS.

CHAK

FEH

...

HOW GOOD OF YOU.

HOW-EVER...

...AS A GUARDIAN.

I DON'T WANT TO PRETEND TO OVERLOOK THINGS LIKE THAT...

THAT MAN...

HE WAS MY GUARDIAN AND MY TEACHER WHEN MY PARENTS WEREN'T AT HOME.

...TOOK CARE OF ME AND MY YOUNGER BROTHER.

BACK THEN I SAW A LEVEL E VAMPIRE FOR THE FIRST TIME...

GRIP

I BLOCKED MY MASTER'S WAY...

...PLEADING WITH HIM THAT SHE WAS A GOOD PERSON...

HE LOST AN EYE DUE TO MY IGNORANCE.

THE DOCTOR AT OUR ELEMENTARY SCHOOL...

...WAS A REALLY NICE, BEAUTIFUL WOMAN.

ONE DAY SHE SUDDENLY TRANSFORMED INTO A FEROCIOUS VAMPIRE RIGHT IN FRONT OF US.

BUT SHE WAS A FORMER HUMAN WHO HAD RUN AWAY FROM AN ARISTOCRAT.

I DIDN'T THINK YOU'D AGREE TO COME HERE, CROSS.

HAS HE NOW BECOME TOO MUCH FOR YOU TO HANDLE?

HOW IS KIRYU'S SON DOING?

OF COURSE NOT... ZERO HASN'T LOST HIS SANITY YET.

THERE'S NOTHING THAT THE HUNTER SOCIETY NEEDS TO WORRY ABOUT...

IT'S REGRETTABLE YOU'RE SUSPICIOUS ABOUT THE PEACE AT CROSS ACADEMY...

HE WILL GET RID OF KIRYU'S SON IF HE DECIDES HE'S BECOME DANGEROUS.

I SENT YAGARI TO YOUR SCHOOL...

I WILL WAIT FOR A REPORT ABOUT THE TRUTH OF THAT.

TMP

VAMPIRE KNIGHT

NINTH NIGHT: CHOICES MADE

I'M...

...SCARED...

GULK

HUFF

GRIP

IF YOU HAVEN'T COMPLETELY LOST YOUR SANITY...

...I WON'T LET YOU DIE.

AT LEAST THAT MEANS YOU HAVEN'T GIVEN UP!

HATE VAMPIRES, HATE ME...

HOW CAN I HATE YOU?

!

OH.

YEAH, I'M OKAY. I'M NOT ANEMIC-- I'M FINE AS USUAL...

I CAN GO TO SCHOOL TOMORROW TOO.

?

ARE YOU... ALL RIGHT?

BOTH OF US...

NOTHING HAS CHANGED.

SWAY

...UNDERSTAND, BUT NEITHER OF US WILL SAY IT.

ZERO, PLEASE COME TO SCHOOL TOMORROW.

PROMISE ME.

YOUR HAIR... IS WET...

SUFF

WHAT WERE YOU WASHING AWAY?

...

OF COURSE HE KNOWS...

OH.

THE PUREBLOOD VAMPIRE HOLDS HER SO GENTLY IN HIS ARMS…

TMP

…BUT OF COURSE YOU REALIZE WHAT SHE'S DONE.

I DON'T GIVE A DAMN WHY YOU TREAT THAT LITTLE GIRL DIFFERENTLY…

YOU MUST BE SEETHING WITH RAGE, RIGHT?

...MADE THAT VOW TO ME.

THAT DAY, YOU YOUR- SELF...

"I'LL MAKE SURE YOU DON'T REGRET LOSING YOUR EYE TO SAVE MY LIFE."

I HAVE NO INTENTION OF SAVING A KID WHO ONLY WANTS TO TAKE THE EASY WAY OUT.

WATCHING YOU RIGHT NOW MADE ME WANT TO KILL YOU FOR REAL.

JUST NOW, YOU DECIDED TO LIVE YOUR LIFE COVERED IN BLOOD.

STRUGGLE UNTIL YOU CAN'T STRUGGLE ANYMORE.

ZERO...

...I REALLY
THOUGHT YOU
WERE GOING
TO DIE.

YUKI...

GRIP

I...

...WILL
NOT
REGRET
MY
DECISION.

NINTH NIGHT/END

IT'S TIME FOR THE CROSS ACADEMY NIGHT CLASS...

...TO RETURN TO THEIR DORM.

WELCOME BACK, NIGHT CLASS.

YUKI CROSS, DAY CLASS, DISCIPLINARY COMMITTEE MEMBER

ZERO KIRYU, DAY CLASS, DISCIPLINARY COMMITTEE MEMBER

IT WAS A QUIET EVENING.

NO, NOT TONIGHT.

ANYTHING UNUSUAL HAPPEN?

WE'RE BACK.

ONLY THE HEADMASTER, WHO IS MY ADOPTED FATHER, AND WE DISCIPLINARY COMMITTEE MEMBERS...

...KNOW THAT EVERYONE IN THE NIGHT CLASS IS A VAMPIRE.

OH REALLY?

WAIT, ZERO!

I-I DIDN'T FORGET MY DUTIES!

WHY'D YOU SIGH LIKE THAT?

THE DISCIPLINARY COMMITTEE IS HERE TO KEEP PEACE IN THE SCHOOL, DAY AND NIGHT...

...SO THAT NO ONE FINDS OUT THE SECRET.

WE ARE ACTUALLY THE SCHOOL GUARDIANS.

...IS YOUR FAVORITE-- THE GINGER STIR-FRY SET.

YOU'LL MISS OUT.

BUT TODAY'S BREAK- FAST...

I JUST GOT INTO BED...

YUKI...

...WAKE UP.

VUMP

165

VI

Recently I've received comments about the manga I drew before Vampire Knight. There are people who have been reading my manga since my very first work... I'm a very fortunate person.(So why what do you think? ♪ Has my manga matured a little? ♪)

To those who are solely devoted to vampires, and to those who have eaten vegetables from Hino's other fields, please keep on reading! ♭

Thank you for your letters. Reading them cheers me up. It's difficult for me to reply, but I'll do my best to pay you back with my work! Thank you so much..!!

In volumes 1 and 2, perhaps Zero was more like the heroine than Yuki? ♪ From now on I plan to have Yuki do her best, like a heroine should. In the next volume, I'm planning on writing these sidebars based on a theme. We should be able to meet again, a bit sooner next time..!

See you!!
Matsuri Hino

YAWN

CHAK

I WILL DEFINITELY MAKE YOU TAKE SUPPLEMENTARY CLASSES.

CROSS! DON'T THINK YOU'LL GET SPECIAL TREATMENT JUST BECAUSE YOU'RE THE HEADMASTER'S DAUGHTER.

ZZZ

OOPS.

YOU'RE LATE AGAIN...

...KIRYU.

GRRRRR

THEY HELP KEEP THINGS PLEASANT.

WE DO NEED THE DISCIPLINARY COMMITTEE.

THERE, STEP BACK! STEP BACK!

HEH

YOU'RE RIGHT.

...MISS DISCIPLINARY COMMITTEE.

THANK YOU...

THE DAILY DUTIES OF THE GUARDIANS START HERE...

NO PROBLEM!

SOMETIMES THERE ARE LAZY DAYS TOO/END

THE EVENING BEFORE THE DAY CLASS ENTRANCE CEREMONY (THREE MONTHS AGO).

...THANK YOU FOR COMING TO THE "FRIENDSHIP EVENING."

TO ALL NEW STUDENTS OF THE DAY CLASS...

YAWN

FRIENDSHIP EVENING
SPONSORED BY HEADMASTER CROSS

THOUGH TO TELL THE TRUTH, THE NIGHT CLASS AND THE DAY CLASS DON'T HAVE A CHANCE OF MEETING TOO OFTEN...

I'M HANABUSA AIDO, REPRESENTING THE NIGHT CLASS.

VAMPIRE KNIGHT

BONUS STORY: I MUST'VE BEEN BORN UNDER THE "VICTIM OF CIRCUMSTANCES" STAR...

SO IT IS TRUE THAT EVERYONE IN THE NIGHT CLASS IS BEAUTIFUL AND ELITE!

...

...UH, I MEAN DORM PRESIDENT KURAN... I'M BEGINNING TO THINK HE'S MAKING ME TAKE CARE OF ALL THE TROUBLESOME STUFF.

FROM BEHIND THE SCENES.

AH, OUR GANG LEADER...

POFF

AND...

I FINALLY BEGIN TO WONDER...

WHY AM I ALWAYS THE VICTIM?

YEAH, AKATSUKI. DON'T CALL HIM BY THAT NAME. IT'S RUDE!

DID YOU CALL HIM "GANG LEADER"?!

"GANG LEADER"?!

HEY, TAKUMA-SAMA!

HA HA HA! YEAH, THAT COULD BE!

ALTHOUGH THERE'S NO PROOF.

AT LEAST CALL HIM "SUPREME GANG LEADER"!

CALLING HIM "GANG LEADER" WOULD RUIN HIS IMAGE!

KANAME-SAMA IS HANDSOME, WELL BEHAVED, AND A PERFECT HONOR STUDENT!

TAK TAK TAK

AND... IT'LL BE MY BIRTH-DAY SOON...

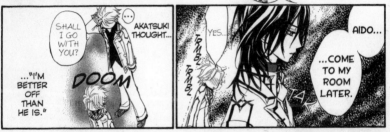

SHALL I GO WITH YOU?

...

AKATSUKI THOUGHT...

..."I'M BETTER OFF THAN HE IS."

DOOM

YES...

TRMBL TRMBL TRMBL

AIDO...

...COME TO MY ROOM LATER.

BONUS STORY: I MUST'VE BEEN BORN UNDER THE "VICTIM OF CIRCUMSTANCES" STAR.../END

VAMPIRES COVERED IN BLOOD ARE PROHIBITED FROM ENTERING THIS PAGE!!

❧ WHAT AM I TO YOU... (EIGHTH NIGHT) ❧

...TEACHER?

OR IS THERE A VAMPIRE AMONG US WHO YOU WANT TO KILL...

...

KANAME-SAMA

DO YOU HATE ME OR SOMETHING?!

AH...

VEEN

EXCUSE ME, MAY I?

YES?

THIS GIRL WILL APPEAR IN VOLUME 3. ♩

This happened just a bit before "Night Class Side" in volume 1.

~ THE BUCKET AND KANAME-SAMA ~

THE BUCKET AND KANAME-SAMA

DON'T MOVE...

...AIDO.

STUFF

'Up

SPLORSH SPLORSH SPLORSH

AAAAH!!!

KANAME-SAMA!

This happened just a bit before "Night Class Side" in volume I

WHAT? AIDO, DID YOU JUST THINK YOU'RE WITNESSING SOMETHING RARE?

YES, KANAME-SAMA.

ONLY I! ONLY I AM WITNESSING THIS RARE EVENT WITH KANAME-SAMA!

KANAME-SAMA IS FILLING IT WITH WATER FROM A HOSE.

KANAME-SAMA IS SMILING, HOLDING A BUCKET.

THIS CAN'T BE HAPPENING!

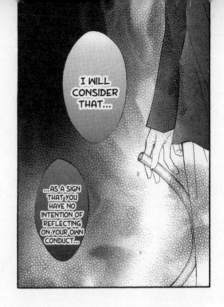

I WILL CONSIDER THAT...

...AS A SIGN THAT YOU HAVE NO INTENTION OF REFLECTING ON YOUR OWN CONDUCT...

～THE EVE BEFORE THE GUARDIANS～
MADE THEIR DEBUT

SO HEAR ME WELL, YUKI...

TOMORROW YOU WILL BECOME THE SCHOOL'S "GUARDIANS."

LISTEN!

THE VAMPIRE KIDS WHO ARE IN THE NIGHT CLASS HAVE A LOT OF PRIDE! THEY'RE FRESH AND ARROGANT!

HOW DO I SAY IT?? THEY'RE LIKE ARISTOCRATS!

EEK!

GUIDE-LINES FOR GUARD-IANS... YUP.

UH-HUH!

SKRTCH SKRTCH

TRY TO BECOME THEIR MASCOT!

BE HUMBLE SO THAT THEY LOVE YOU.

SO!

THAT'S BECAUSE THEY ARE ARISTO-CRATS.

TRUE ONES.

...EVENTUALLY YOU'LL BE JOINING TH--

AS YOU KNOW...

DO YOUR BEST TO HAVE EVERY-ONE IN THE NIGHT CLASS LIKE YOU.

BECOME THEIR MASCOT.

ZERO, YOU TOO.

SKRTCH SKRTCH

...

GASP

GRIB

BY THE WAY, YOU USED TO GO ON PATROL, RIGHT, HEAD-MASTER?

NOT PAYING ATTENTION

GRIB GRIB

WHAT ARE YOU SAYING?!

GRIB GRIB GRIB

184

WELL, YES.

...

?

GRIB

HERE'S A GOOD EXAMPLE...

BUT YOU KNOW, VAMPIRES ARE BASICALLY YANKIS AND ARE QUITE SCARY...

～KANAME... (NINTH NIGHT)～

KANAME...

...DOES THAT MEAN THAT EVEN AFTER TEN YEARS, I STILL HAVE NO BOOBS?

SO IT SEEMS...

IN TEN YEARS...

...THAT'S THE ONLY THING THAT HAS CHANGED.

ALONG WITH THE HEAD-MASTER...

I REALIZE NOW THAT THIS IS THE ONLY THING I CAN DO FOR YOU.

ZERO!

THE HEAD-MASTER?

?

...

DASH

SORRY!!

WAIT A SEC! I'LL GO GET THE HEAD-MASTER!

...

YOU CAN DRINK MORE BLOOD FROM THE HEAD-MASTER.

YOU CAN SUCK HIM DRY IF YOU WANT TO.

TMP
TMP

VAMPIRES COVERED IN BLOOD ARE PROHIBITED FROM ENTERING THIS PAGE/END

The
Night Class
Kettle Club

To those who give me the power to draw my manga, my readers.
To my editor in faraway Tokyo, who always supports me when I get tediously stubborn and retrospective.
To O. Mio-sama, K. Midori-sama, and M. Kaoru-sama, who help me with my manuscripts.
To my childhood friend F. Natsuki-sama, who gracefully lets me use Ichijo-senpai's name.
And to my mother and my dear friends who always help me at various times.

I thank you all from the bottom of my heart!   I've got to do better!! Yeah.

樋野まつり
Matsuri Hino

EDITOR'S NOTES

Characters

Matsuri Hino puts careful thought into the names of her characters in *Vampire Knight*. Below is the collection of characters through volume 2. Each character's name is presented family name first, per the kanji reading.

黒主優姫

Cross Yuki

Yuki's last name, *Kurosu*, is the Japanese pronunciation of the English word "cross." However, the kanji has a different meaning—*kuro* means "black" and *su* means "master." Her first name is a combination of *yuu*, meaning "tender" or "kind," and *ki*, meaning "princess."

錐生零

Kiryu Zero

Zero's first name is the kanji for *rei*, meaning "zero." In his last name, *Kiryu*, the *ki* means "auger" or "drill," and the *ryu* means "life."

玖蘭枢

Kuran Kaname

Kaname means "hinge" or "door." The kanji for his last name is a combination of the old-fashioned way of writing *ku*, meaning "nine," and *ran*, meaning "orchid": "nine orchids."

藍堂英

Aido Hanabusa

Hanabusa means "petals of a flower." *Aido* means "indigo temple." In Japanese, the pronunciation of *Aido* is very close to the pronunciation of the English word *idol*.

架院暁

Kain Akatsuki

Akatsuki means "dawn," or "day-break." In *Kain*, *ka* is a base or support, while *in* denotes a building that has high fences around it, such as a temple or school.

早園瑠佳

Souen Ruka

In *Ruka*, the *ru* means "lapis lazuli" while the *ka* means "good-looking," or "beautiful." The *sou* in Ruka's surname, *Souen*, means "early," but this kanji also has an obscure meaning of "strong fragrance." The *en* means "garden."

一条 拓麻

Ichijo Takuma

Ichijo can mean a "ray" or "streak." The kanji for *Takuma* is a combination of *taku*, meaning "to cultivate" and *ma*, which is the kanji for *asa*, meaning "hemp" or "flax," a plant with blue flowers.

支葵千里

Shiki Senri

Shiki's last name is a combination of *shi*, meaning "to support" and *ki*, meaning "mallow"—a flowering plant with pink or white blossoms. The *ri* in *Senri* is a traditional Japanese unit of measure for distance, and one *ri* is about 2.44 miles. Senri means "1,000 *ri*."

夜刈十牙

Yagari Toga

Yagari is a combination of *ya*, meaning "night," and *gari*, meaning "to harvest." *Toga* means "ten fangs."

Terms

Night Class/Kettle Club: This is a pun. When written differently in Japanese, "Night Class" can also mean "Kettle Club."

-sama: The suffix *sama* is used in formal address for someone who ranks higher in the social hierarchy. The vampires call their leader "Kaname-sama" only when they are among their own kind.

-sensei: This suffix is used for respected professionals, such as teachers, doctors, and mangaka.

yanki: A *yanki* is a juvenile delinquent or young gangster.

Matsuri Hino burst onto the manga scene with her series *Kono Yume ga Sametara* (When This Dream Is Over), which was published in *LaLa DX* magazine. Hino was a manga artist a mere nine months after she decided to become one.

With the success of her popular series *Captive Hearts* and *MeruPuri*, Hino has established herself as a major player in the world of shojo manga. *Vampire Knight* is currently serialized in *LaLa* magazine.

Hino enjoys creative activities and has commented that she would have been either an architect or an apprentice to traditional Japanese craft masters if she had not become a manga artist.

VAMPIRE KNIGHT
Vol. 2
Shojo Beat Edition

This manga contains material that was originally published in English in *Shojo Beat* magazine, December 2006–February 2007 issues.

STORY AND ART BY
MATSURI HINO

Translation & English Adaptation/Tomo Kimura
Touch-up Art & Lettering/Mark McMurray & George Caltsoudas
Graphic Design/Amy Martin
Editor/Nancy Thistlethwaite

VP, Production/Alvin Lu
VP, Sales & Product Marketing/Gonzalo Ferreyra
VP, Creative/Linda Espinosa
Publisher/Hyoe Narita

Vampire Knight by Matsuri Hino © Matsuri Hino 2005. All rights reserved. First published in Japan in 2005 by HAKUSENSHA, Inc., Tokyo. English language translation rights arranged with HAKUSENSHA, Inc., Tokyo.

The rights of the author(s) of the work(s) in this publication to be so identified have been asserted in accordance with the Copyright, Designs and Patents Act 1988. A CIP catalogue record for this book is available from the British Library.

Printed in Canada

Published by VIZ Media, LLC
P.O. Box 77010
San Francisco, CA 94107

10 9 8 7
First printing, May 2007
Seventh printing, September 2009

www.viz.com

www.shojobeat.com

Tell us what you think about Shojo Beat Manga!

Our survey is now available online. Go to:

shojobeat.com/mangasurvey

Help us make our product offerings better!

THE REAL DRAMA BEGINS IN...